Non-verbal Reasoning
Rapid Tests 4

Rebecca Brant

4-5 6-7

Oliver

Schofield&Sims

Introduction

This book gives you practice in answering non-verbal reasoning questions quickly.

The questions are like the questions on the 11+ and other school selection tests. You must find the correct answers.

School selection tests are usually timed, so you need to get used to working quickly. Each test has a target time for you to work towards. You should time how long you spend on each test, or you can ask an adult to time you.

All the questions in this book are multiple choice. For each question you are given a choice of answers. Choose the answer you think is correct and draw a circle round the letter beneath it.

What you need

- A pencil
- An eraser
- A clock, watch or stopwatch
- A sheet of rough paper
- An adult to help you work out how long you take and to mark the test for you

What to do

- Turn to **Section 1 Test 1** on page 4. Look at the grey box at the top of the page labelled **Target time**. This tells you how long the test should take.
- When you are ready to start, write down the time or start the stopwatch. Or the adult helping you will tell you to begin.
- Find this black arrow ⬇ near the top of the first page. Start each test here.
- Find this square ■. The instructions for the first set of questions are beside it. Read them carefully.
- Look below the instructions. Read the **Example**. Work out why the answer given is correct.
- Using similar methods, answer each question.
- Try to answer every question. If you do get stuck on a question, leave it and go on to the next one. Work quickly and try your best.
- When you have finished the first page, go straight on to the next page without waiting. Here you will find a different question type. Again, read the instructions and the example. Then answer the questions.
- When you reach the end, stop. Write down the time or stop the stopwatch. Or tell the adult that you have finished.
- With the adult, work out how long you took to do the test. Fill in the **Time taken** box at the end of the test.
- The adult will mark your test and fill in the **Score** and **Target met?** boxes.
- Turn to the **Progress chart** on page 40. Write your score in the box and colour in the graph to show how many questions you got right.
- Did you get some questions wrong? You should always have another go at them before you look at the answers. Then ask the adult to check your work and help you if you are still not sure.
- Later, you will do some more of these tests. You will soon learn to work through them more quickly. The adult who is helping you will tell you what to do next.

Published by **Schofield & Sims Ltd**,
7 Mariner Court, Wakefield, West Yorkshire WF4 3FL, UK
Telephone 01484 607080
www.schofieldandsims.co.uk
First published in 2014
This edition copyright © Schofield & Sims Ltd, 2018
Sixth impression 2021
Author: **Rebecca Brant**. Rebecca Brant has asserted her moral right under the Copyright, Designs and Patents Act, 1988, to be identified as the author of this work.
British Library Cataloguing in Publication Data. A catalogue record for this book is available from the British Library.

Commissioned by **Carolyn Richardson Publishing Services**

Design by **Oxford Designers & Illustrators**
Front cover design by **Ledgard Jepson Ltd**
Printed in the UK by **Page Bros (Norwich) Ltd**
ISBN 978 07217 1466 0

Contents

Which picture on the right belongs to the group on the left? Circle the letter.

Example

a   b   c   d   e

1.   a   b   c   d   e

2.   a   b   c   d   e

3.   a   b   c   d   e

4.   a   b   c   d   e

5.   a   b   c   d   e

6.   a   b   c   d   e

Now go on to the next page ➡

Which picture is the odd one out? Circle the letter.

Example

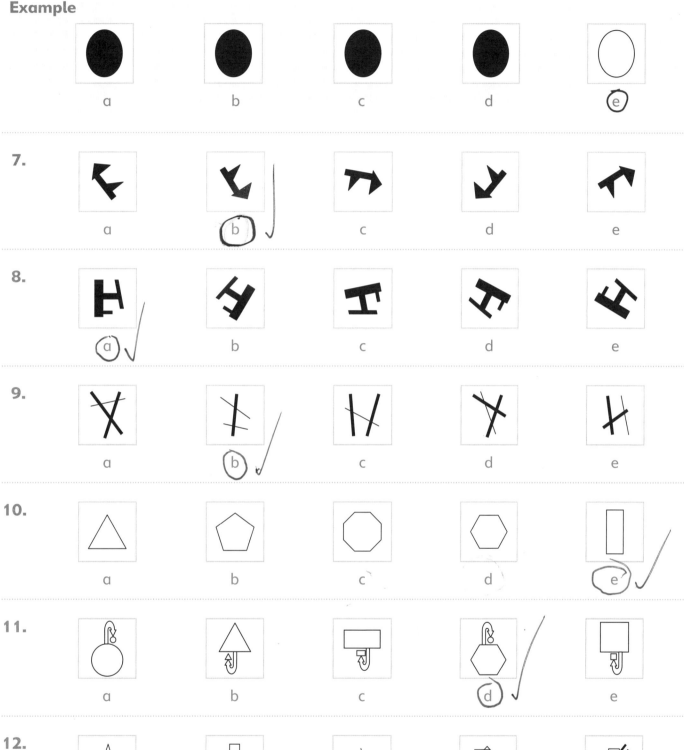

7.

a   b   c   d   e

8.

a   b   c   d   e

9.

a   b   c   d   e

10.

a   b   c   d   e

11.

a   b   c   d   e

12.

a   b   c   d   e

End of test

Score:		Time taken:		Target met?	

Which of the five pictures on the right goes with the third one to make a pair like the two on the left? Circle the letter.

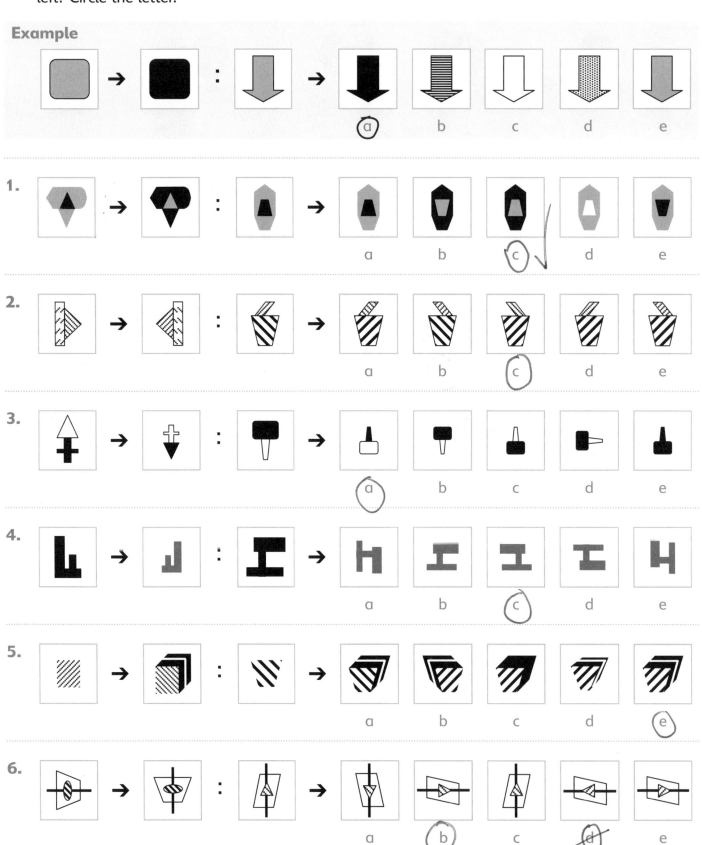

Example

1.

2.

3.

4.

5.

6.

Now go on to the next page ➡

Which picture on the right goes in the empty space? Circle the letter.

Example

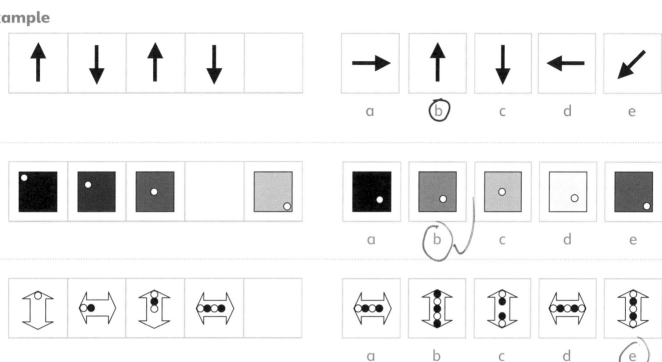

7.

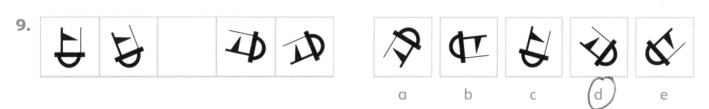

8.

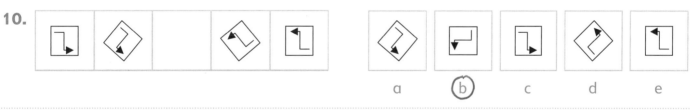

9.

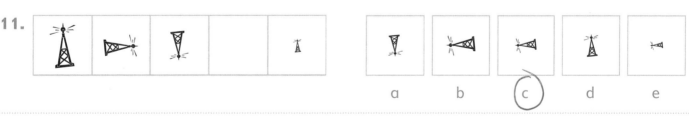

10.

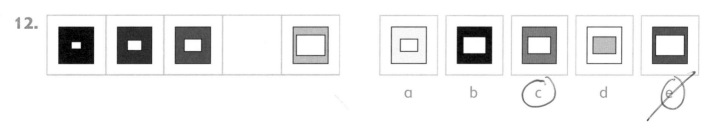

11.

12.

End of test

Score:		Time taken:		Target met?	

In which picture on the right is the picture on the left hidden? Circle the letter.

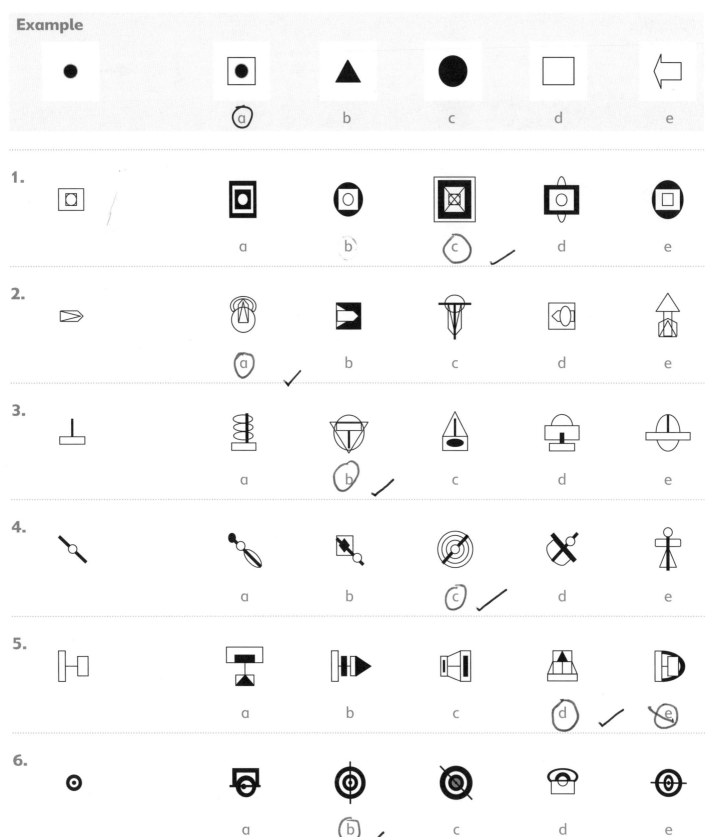

Example

a b c d e

1.

a b c d e

2.

a b c d e

3.

a b c d e

4.

a b c d e

5.

a b c d e

6.

a b c d e

Now go on to the next page ➡

Which picture on the right is a reflection of the picture on the left? Circle the letter.

Example

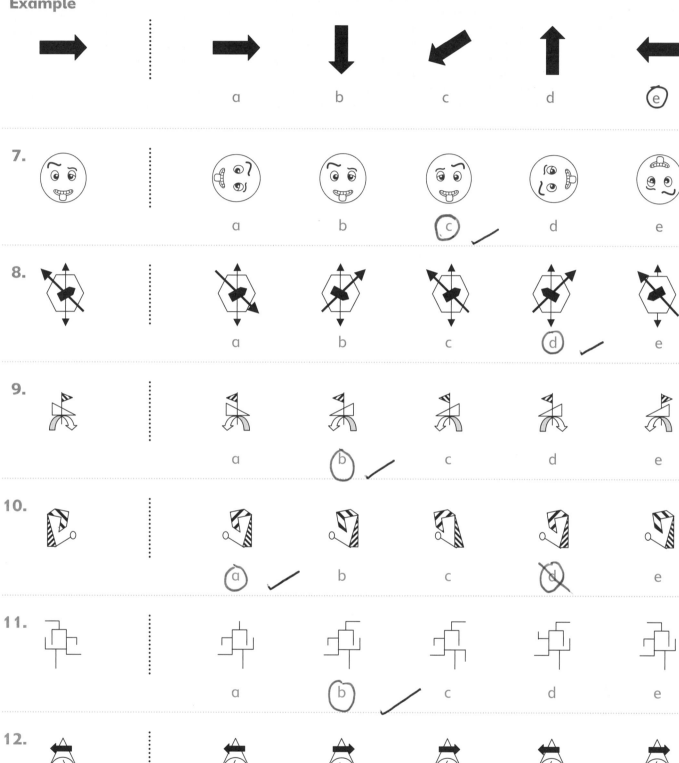

7.

8.

9.

10.

11.

12.

12/12

End of test

Score: 10/12.   Time taken: 5 min's   Target met?

Non-verbal Reasoning Rapid Tests 4

Target time: **7 minutes**

Which picture on the right best fits into the space in the grid? Circle the letter.

Example

a b c d e

1.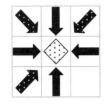

a b c d e

2.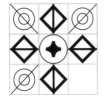

a b c d e

3.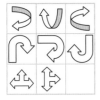

a b c d e

4.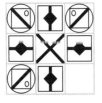

a b c d e

5.

a b c d e

6.

a b c d e

Now go on to the next page ➡

Which picture on the right can be made by combining the first two shapes? Circle the letter.

Example

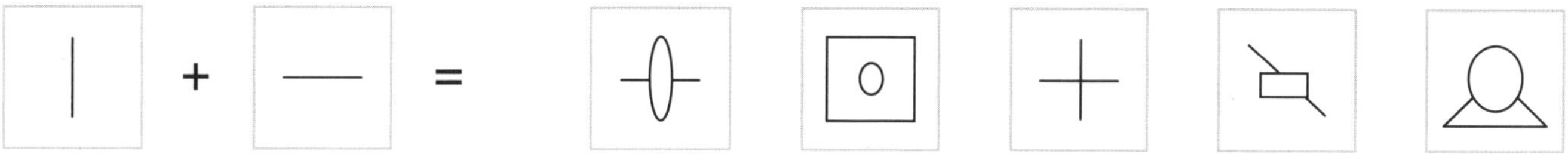

a   b   c   d   e

7.

a   b   c   e

8.

a   b   c   d   e

9.

a   b   c   d   e

10.

a   b   c   d   e

11.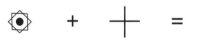

a   b   c   d   e

12.

a   b   c   d   e

End of test

| Score: | | Time taken: | | Target met? | |

Section 1 Test 5

Which net can be made exactly from the cube? Circle the letter.

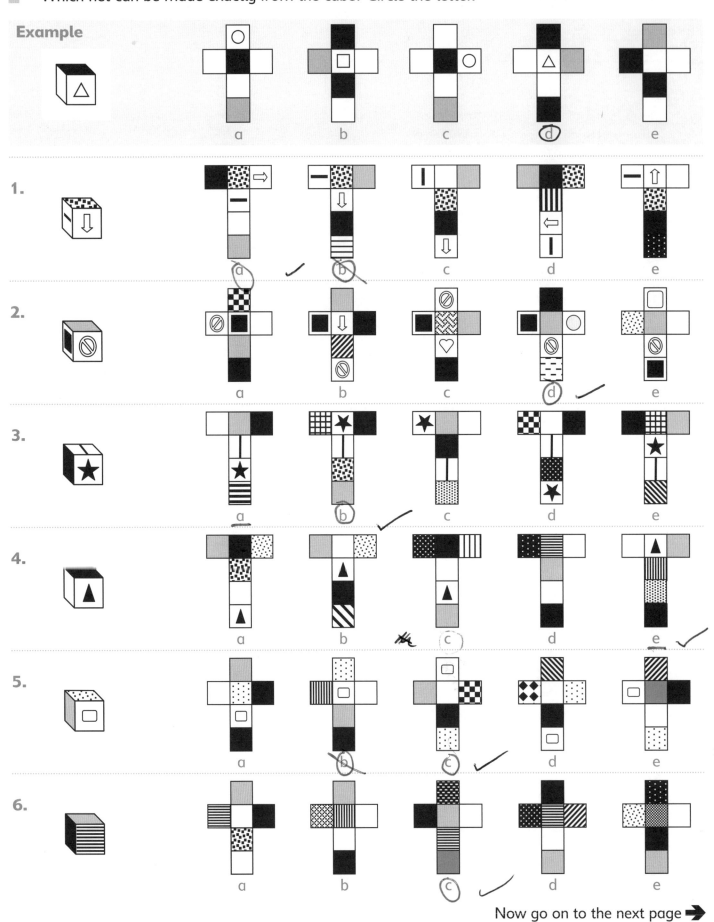

Now go on to the next page ➡

What is the code of the final picture? Circle the letter.

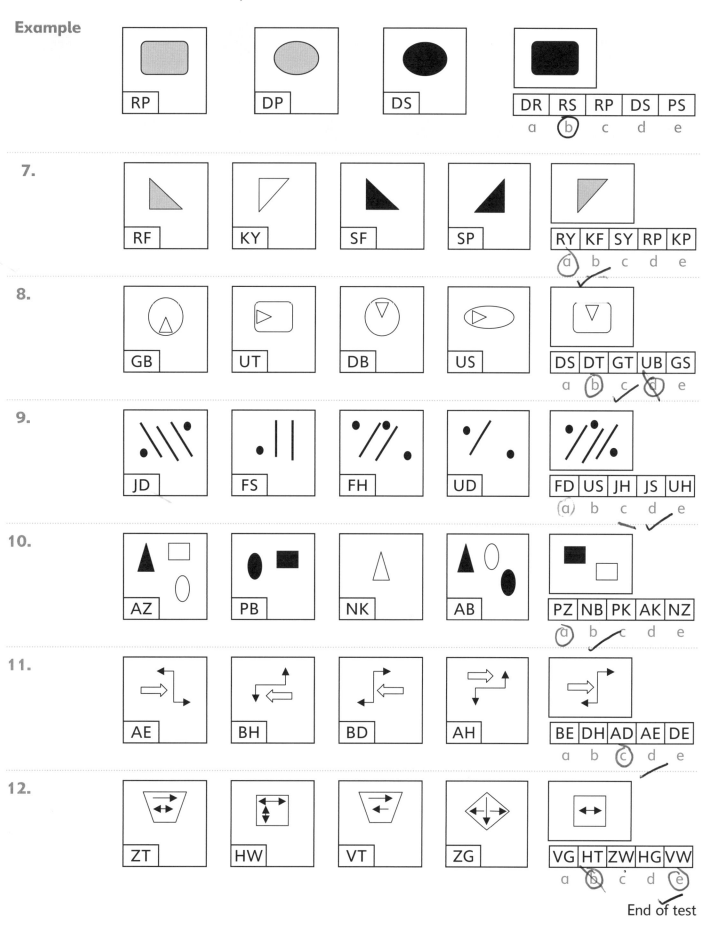

Example

RP | DP | DS | DR | RS | RP | DS | PS
a | b | c | d | e

7.

RF | KY | SF | SP | RY | KF | SY | RP | KP
a | b | c | d | e

8.

GB | UT | DB | US | DS | DT | GT | UB | GS
a | b | c | d | e

9.

JD | FS | FH | UD | FD | US | JH | JS | UH
a | b | c | d | e

10.

AZ | PB | NK | AB | PZ | NB | PK | AK | NZ
a | b | c | d | e

11.

AE | BH | BD | AH | BE | DH | AD | AE | DE
a | b | c | d | e

12.

ZT | HW | VT | ZG | VG | HT | ZW | HG | VW
a | b | c | d | e

End of test

Score:		Time taken:		Target met?	

Which picture on the right belongs to the group on the left? Circle the letter.

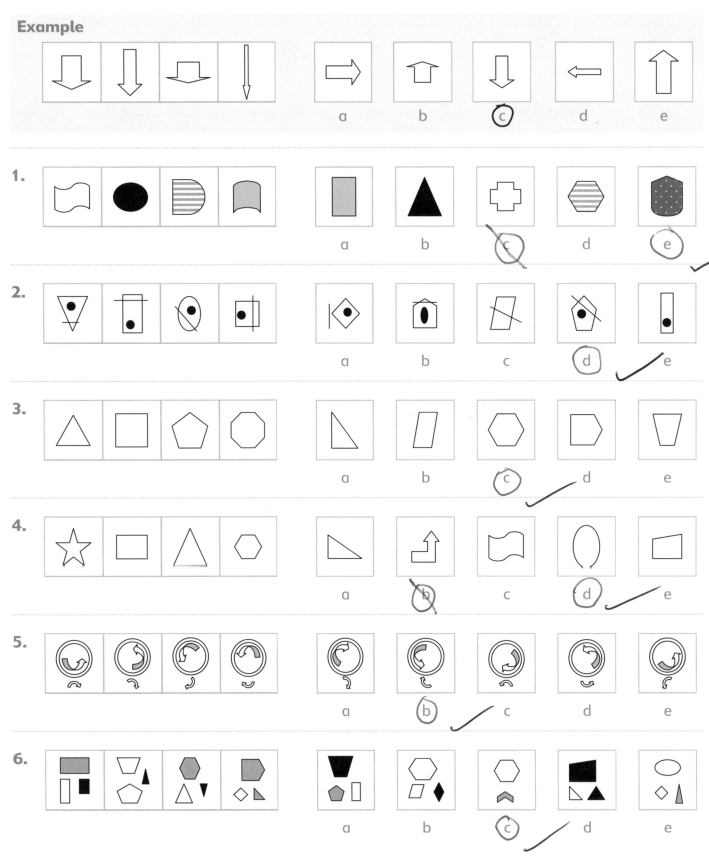

Now go on to the next page ➡

Which of the five pictures on the right goes with the third one to make a pair like the two on the left? Circle the letter.

Example

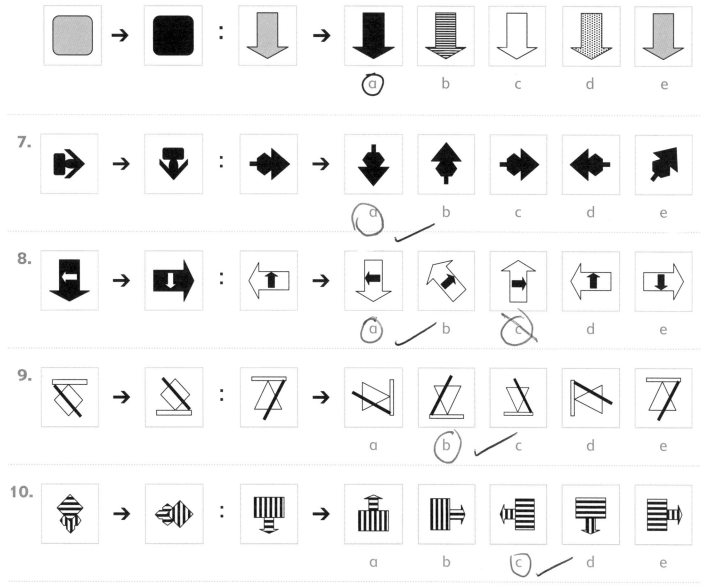

7.

8.

9.

10.

11.

12.

End of test

| Score: | 12/12 | Time taken: | | Target met? | |

Target time: **7 minutes**

Which picture on the right goes in the empty space? Circle the letter.

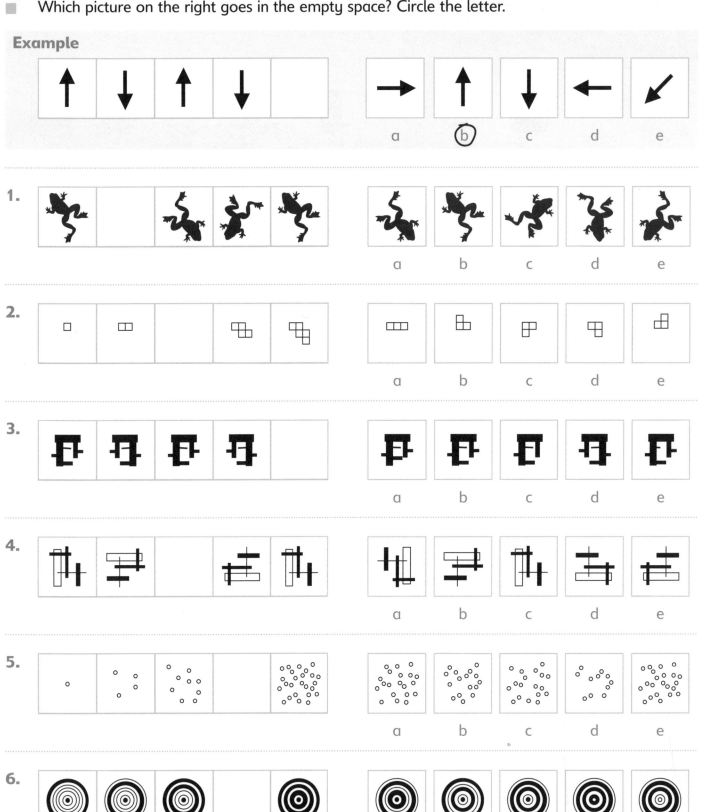

In which picture on the right is the picture on the left hidden? Circle the letter.

Example

                 ⓐ   b   c   d   e

7.

                 a   b   c   d   e

8.

                 a   b   c   d   e

9.

                 a   b   c   d   e

10.

                 a   b   c   d   e

11.

                 a   b   c   d   e

12.

                 a   b   c   d   e

End of test

Score:	Time taken:	Target met?

Target time: **7 minutes**

Which picture on the right is a reflection of the picture on the left? Circle the letter.

Example

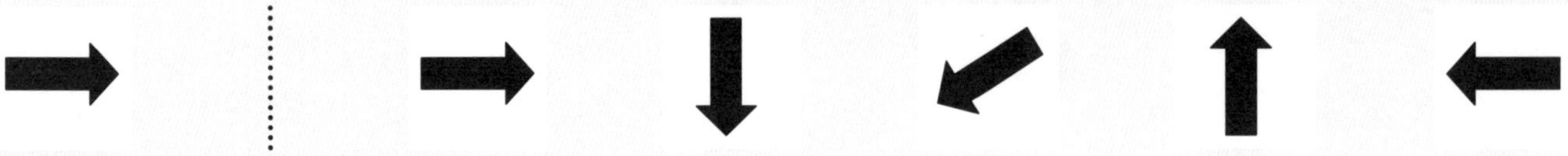

a b c d e

1. 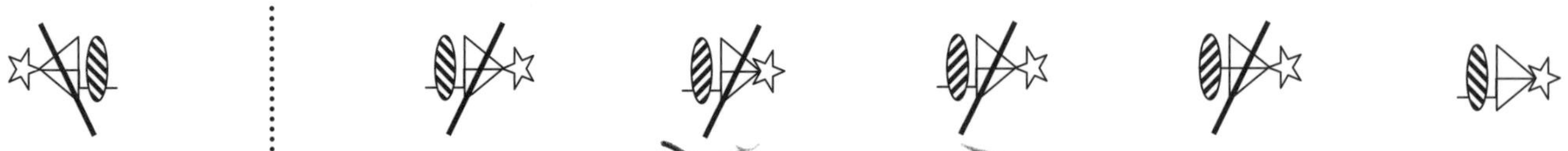

a b c d e

2. 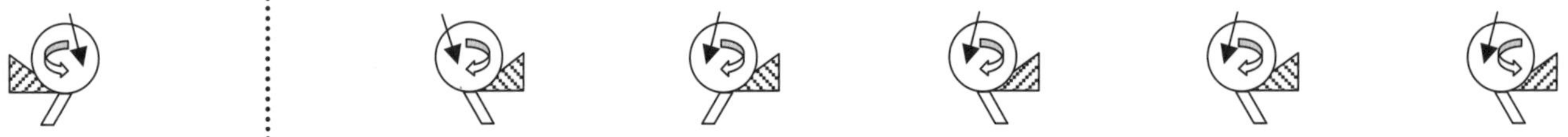

a b c d e

3. 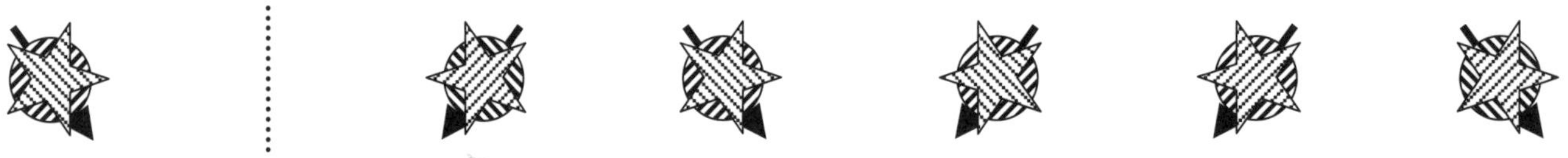

a b c d e

4. 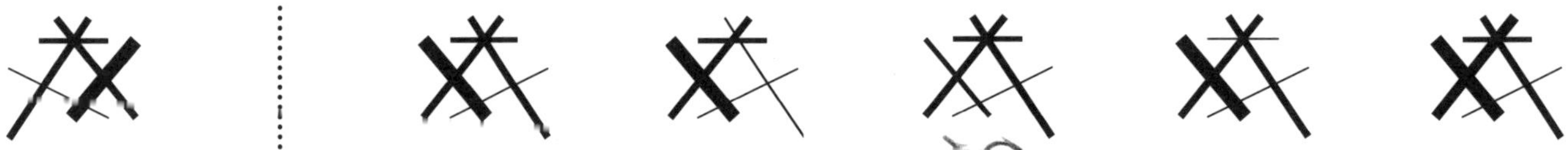

a b c d e

5. 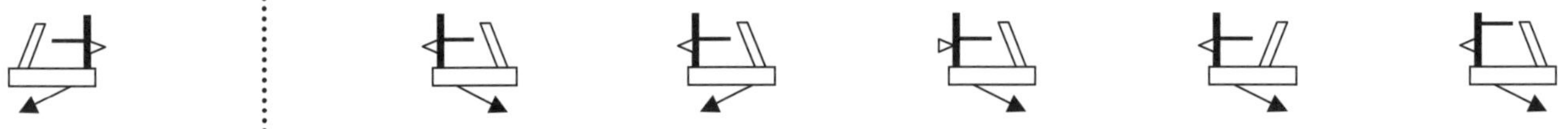

a b c d e

6. 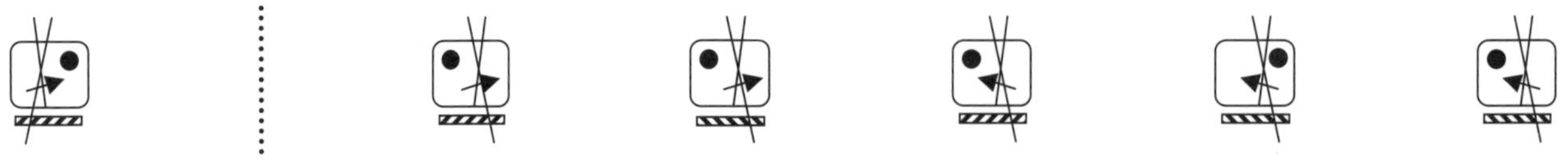

a b c d e

Now go on to the next page

Which picture is the odd one out? Circle the letter.

Example

a   b   c   d   e

7.

a   b   c   d   e

8.

a   b   c   d   e

9.

a   b   c   d   e

10.

a   b   c   d   e

11.

a   b   c   d   e

12.

a   b   c   d   e

End of test

Score:		Time taken:		Target met?	

Which picture on the right can be made by combining the first two shapes? Circle the letter.

Example

 + =

    a   b   ⓒ   d   e

1.

    a   ⓑ   c   d   e

2.

    a   ⓑ   c   d   e

3.

    a   b   ~~c~~   ⓓ   e

4.

    ⓐ   b   c   d   e

5.

    a   ~~b~~   c   ⓓ   e

6.

    a   ⓑ   c   d   e

Now go on to the next page ➡

Non-verbal Reasoning Rapid Tests 4 Answers

Notes for parents, tutors, teachers and other adult helpers

- **Non-verbal Reasoning Rapid Tests 4** is designed for nine- and ten year-olds, but may also be suitable for some children of other ages.

- Remove this pull-out section before giving the book to the child.

- Before the child begins work on the first test, together read the instructions headed **What to do** on page 2. As you do so, point out to the child the different elements in **Section 1 Test 1**.

- Make sure that the child understands how to answer multiple choice questions and has a pencil, an eraser and a sheet of rough paper. Also ensure that the child is able to see a clock or a watch.

- Explain to the child how he or she should go about timing the test. Alternatively, you may wish to time the test yourself. When the child has finished the test, together work out the **Time taken** and complete the box that appears at the end of the test.

- Mark the child's work using this pull-out section, giving one mark for each correct answer. There are a total of 12 marks available for each test. Then complete the **Score** box at the end of the test.

- This table shows you how to mark the **Target met?** box and the **Action** notes help you to plan the next step. However, these are suggestions only. Please use your own judgement as you decide how best to proceed.

Score	Time taken	Target met?	Action
1–6	Any	Not yet	Give the child the previous book in the series. Provide help and support as needed.
7–9	Any	Not yet	Encourage the child to keep practising using the tests in this book. The child may need to repeat some tests. If so, wait a few weeks or the child may simply remember the correct answers. Provide help and support as needed.
10–12	Over target – child took too long	Not yet	
10–12	On target – child took suggested time or less	Yes	Encourage the child to keep practising using further tests in this book, and to move on to the next book when you think this is appropriate.

- After finishing each test, the child should fill in the **Progress chart** on page 40.

- Whatever the test score, always encourage the child to have another go at the questions that he or she got wrong – without looking at the solutions. If the child's answers are still incorrect, work through these questions together. Demonstrate the correct method if necessary.

- If the child struggles with particular question types, help him or her to develop the strategies needed.

Answers

Section 1 Test 1
(pages 4–5)

1. **e** Each picture contains an 'S'-shaped line with two lines crossing it and a rectangle at the end.
2. **a** Each picture contains an arrow with three lines – the two outer lines are identical and the centre line is different.
3. **e** Each picture contains a large white oval overlapping a white shape, and a black oval (note the overlap).
4. **b** Each picture contains a shape with a thick black outline around a grey rhombus.
5. **c** Each picture is a rotation (not a reflection).
6. **d** Each picture contains a shape with a black circle on its right-hand side.
7. **b** The others are all rotations of the same picture (whereas **b** is a reflection).
8. **a** The others are all rotations of the same picture (whereas **a** is a reflection).
9. **b** The others all have two thick lines and one thin line.
10. **e** The others are all regular shapes.
11. **d** The big shape and the small shape at the end of the arrow are identical in the other pictures.
12. **c** The others all have parallel lines crossing them.

Section 1 Test 2
(pages 6–7)

1. **c** The picture swaps colours.
2. **c** The picture is reflected in the vertical mirror line.
3. **a** The picture is reflected in the horizontal mirror line, gets smaller and the colours are swapped.
4. **c** The picture is reflected in the vertical mirror line, gets smaller and changes from black to grey.
5. **e** The 2D shape becomes 3D to the right, the stripes are reflected and there is a white band between thick black bands.

6. **b** The picture is rotated 90° clockwise and the stripes are reflected.
7. **b** The square gets paler and the circle moves diagonally from top left to bottom right.
8. **e** The direction of the arrow alternates and one circle in an alternating colour is added each time.
9. **d** The picture is rotated slightly anticlockwise.
10. **b** The picture is rotated 45° clockwise each time.
11. **c** The picture is rotated 90° clockwise and gets smaller.
12. **c** The square gets paler and the internal rectangle gets bigger.

Section 1 Test 3
(pages 8–9)

1. **c**

2. **a**

3. **b**

4. **c**

5. **d**

6. **b**

7. **c** (note the eyebrows)

8. **d**

9. **b** (note direction of stripes)

10. **a** (note direction of stripes)

11. **b**

Schofield & Sims

12. e

Section 1 Test 4
(pages 10–11)

1. d Reflective pattern
2. c Reflective pattern
3. a The picture in each row is rotated 90° clockwise.
4. d Reflective pattern
5. b There are three black shapes in the patterns in the bottom row.
6. e The picture in each row is rotated 45° clockwise.
7. e

8. b

9. a

10. e

11. b

12. a

Section 1 Test 5
(pages 12–13)

If in doubt about the nets of cubes, copy them onto a piece of paper and fold them up.

1. a   **4. e**
2. d   **5. c**
3. b   **6. c**
7. a First letter – colour
Second letter – triangle position
8. b First letter – triangle direction
Second letter – outer shape
9. c First letter – number of lines
Second letter – number of circles
10. a First letter – number of shapes
Second letter – number of black shapes
11. c First letter – wide arrow direction
Second letter – angled arrow direction

12. e First letter – number of arrow heads
Second letter – shape

Section 1 Test 6
(pages 14–15)

1. e Each picture contains a curved line.
2. d Each picture contains a line crossing the large white shape and a black circle.
3. c Each picture contains a regular shape.
4. d Each picture contains a symmetrical shape.
5. b Each picture contains an internal arrow facing anticlockwise and an external arrow facing clockwise.
6. c Each picture contains 12 sides.
7. a The picture is rotated 90° clockwise.
8. a The picture is rotated 90° anticlockwise.
9. b The picture is rotated 180°.
10. c The picture is rotated 90° clockwise.
11. a The picture is reflected in the vertical mirror line.
12. e The picture is rotated 180°.

Section 2 Test 1
(pages 16–17)

1. c The picture is rotated 90° clockwise.
2. d One square is added in the correct order each time (**b** is too high).
3. b Repeating pattern
4. a The picture is rotated 90° clockwise.
5. b The number of circles increases as square numbers (1, 4, 9, 16, 25).
6. c Concentric black circles move towards the black central circle.
7. e

8. a

9. b

10. a

11. e

12. c

Answers

Section 2 Test 2
(pages 18–19)

1. c   (note star and thin line)

2. d

3. a

4. a   (note line thickness)

5. a

6. e   (note direction of of stripes)

7. c The others all have the same number of lines as there are sides on the shape.

8. b In all the others, half the diamond is inside the rectangle.

9. b In all the others, the black circles overlap the edge of the white shape.

10. d The others all contain a triangle, an oval and a rectangle.

11. e The others all have two identical small shapes either side of the line.

12. d The others all have three arrow heads.

Section 2 Test 3
(pages 20–21)

1. b

2. b

3. d

4. a

5. d

6. b

7. b First letter – line position
Second letter – number of stars

8. e First letter – colour
Second letter – shape

9. a First letter – shading
Second letter – number of horizontal lines

10. c First letter – arrow direction
Second letter – circle colour

11. a First letter – 'L' shape position
Second letter – number of lines

12. e First letter – size of circle
Second letter – number of lines

Section 2 Test 4
(pages 22–23)

1. c Reflective pattern

2. e Reflective pattern (note orientation of small stars)

3. b The corners are rotated 90° clockwise (reflective pattern).

4. a It is a reflection, in the horizontal mirror line, of the top central square.

5. b Along each row, the shape increases by one and is rotated 90° clockwise.

6. b The external middle squares are rotated 90°.

If in doubt about the nets of cubes, copy them onto a piece of paper and fold them up.

7. b

8. d

9. d

10. e

11. b

12. e

Section 2 Test 5
(pages 24–25)

1. **d**

2. **b**

3. **b**

4. **e**

5. **c**

6. **a**

7. **b** There are the same number of smaller shapes as there are number of sides on the big shape.
8. **c** The picture is reflected in the horizontal mirror line.
9. **d** The picture is rotated 90° anticlockwise.
10. **b** The picture is reflected in the vertical mirror line.
11. **e** The picture is rotated 90° anticlockwise.
12. **a** The stripes are reflected and the two internal shapes swap size.

Section 2 Test 6
(pages 26–27)

1. **c** First letter – rectangle position
   Second letter – number of circles
2. **b** First letter – number of arrows
   Second letter – arrow direction
3. **d** First letter – outer shape
   Second letter – number of triangles
4. **c** First letter – rectangle colour
   Second letter – number of ovals above and below the line
5. **e** First letter – shading
   Second letter – arrow direction
6. **b** First letter – line position
   Second letter – stripe direction

7. **a** The two outer shapes are the same and are made from the same type of line.
8. **a** Each picture contains five rectangles.
9. **b** Each picture contains three of the same shape in the same colour on the line.
10. **b** Each picture has a white arrow and a black arrow on the same side of the shape.
11. **e** Each picture has a line of symmetry.
12. **d** Each picture has five places where the arrows and lines cross.

Section 3 Test 1
(pages 28–29)

1. **a** The others all have three linked circles and one separate circle.
2. **d** The others all have an odd number of stars.
3. **b** The others all have two shapes made from broken lines.
4. **e** The others all have two single arrows pointing in the same direction.
5. **b** The others all have arrows pointing in four different directions.
6. **a** The others are all rotations of the same shape whereas **a** is a reflection.
7. **c** The rectangle gets darker, the small square moves to the left, and the line moves to the right.
8. **c** Repeating pattern
9. **e** A rectangle and a curved rectangle are added alternately.
10. **e** The picture is rotated 45° anticlockwise each time.
11. **b** The line gets lighter, the circle gets darker, and the circle also moves down the line on alternating sides.
12. **a** One star leaves the triangle each time and then stays in the same place outside it.

Answers

Section 3 Test 2
(pages 30–31)

1. d

2. e

3. a

4. b

5. e

6. d

7. a In each row, the thick black line moves towards the centre.

8. a The arrow is rotated 90° anticlockwise and the colour alternates across the rows.

9. b On each row, the picture is rotated 90° clockwise.

10. c Reflective pattern

11. a More of the shape appears along the row.

12. b The shape increases by one across the rows and it is in the correct position on a line of the correct thickness.

Section 3 Test 3
(pages 32–33)

If in doubt about the nets of cubes, copy them onto a piece of paper and fold them up.

1. e
2. d
3. c
4. b
5. e
6. c

7. c

8. a

9. c

10. d

11. c

12. b

Section 3 Test 4
(pages 34–35)

1. d The block arrow is rotated 90° anticlockwise, while the internal arrow is rotated 90° clockwise.

2. d The picture is rotated 90° clockwise.

3. c One side is added each time.

4. b The line is rotated 45° clockwise, while the circle moves along the line alternating sides.

5. b The rectangle is rotating 45° clockwise and alternating black and white. The star is rotating 45° anticlockwise and alternating black and white and remains at the same end of the rectangle as it rotates.

6. b The colours are moving inwards.

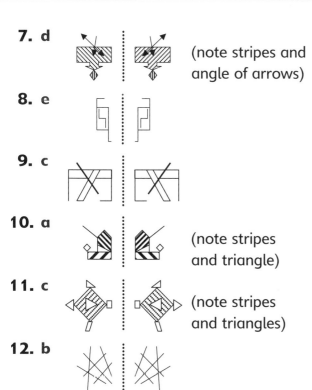

7. d (note stripes and angle of arrows)

8. e

9. c

10. a (note stripes and triangle)

11. c (note stripes and triangles)

12. b

Section 3 Test 5
(pages 36–37)

1. e First letter – arrow line style
Second letter – outline thickness

2. a First letter – central shape
Second letter – outer shape shading

3. e First letter – circle position
Second letter – central shape colour

4. b First letter – circle position
Second letter – line thickness

5. d First letter – arrow colour
Second letter – line thickness

6. c First letter – arrow position
Second letter – arc position

7. a In each row from left to right, one shape is added each time but it is getting thinner and the picture is rotated 90° anticlockwise.

8. a The outer middle square is rotated 90°.

9. e Reflective pattern (note line thickness of circles)

10. d Reflective corner pattern

11. b There are three of each picture, one of each per row/column.

12. b In each row, the correct style of arrow for the row is rotated 90° clockwise, and the correct style of line moves along the arrow.

Section 3 Test 6
(pages 38–39)

1. d Each picture contains a triangle and a circle and a line which is parallel to the triangle.

2. a Each picture contains a solid black arrow crossing the shape.

3. b Each picture contains a total of 10 sides within a large oval.

4. c Each picture contains an arrow with a small shape inside it and a large shape connected to it. Both shapes are the same except for their size and one is black.

5. d Each picture contains a curved rectangle, an arrow, a white rhombus and a small black rectangle.

6. b Each picture contains the same number of lines as there are sides on the shape.

7. e The picture is reflected in the vertical mirror line and the colours are swapped.

8. c The picture is rotated 180°.

9. c The picture is rotated 90° clockwise.

10. d The outer shape is reflected in the horizontal mirror line. The arrow remains pointing in the same direction but changes from black to white.

11. e The picture is rotated 90° anticlockwise, the colours are swapped and the internal shapes get slightly bigger.

12. b The arrow heads move to the opposite end of the lines.

This book of answers is a pull-out section from
Non-verbal Reasoning Rapid Tests 4

Published by **Schofield & Sims Ltd**,
7 Mariner Court, Wakefield, West Yorkshire WF4 3FL, UK
Telephone 01484 607080
www.schofieldandsims.co.uk

First published in 2014
This edition copyright © Schofield & Sims Ltd, 2018
Sixth impression 2021

Author: **Rebecca Brant**
Rebecca Brant has asserted her moral right under the Copyright, Designs and Patents Act, 1988, to be identified as the author of this work.

British Library Cataloguing in Publication Data
A catalogue record for this book is available from the British Library.

Commissioned by **Carolyn Richardson Publishing Services**

Design by **Oxford Designers & Illustrators**
Printed in the UK by **Page Bros (Norwich) Ltd**

ISBN 978 07217 1466 0

What is the code of the final picture? Circle the letter.

Example

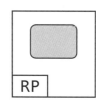 RP

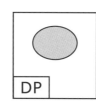 DP

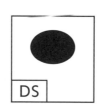 DS

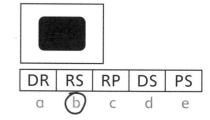

DR	RS	RP	DS	PS
a	ⓑ	c	d	e

7.

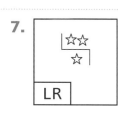 LR

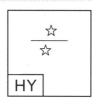 HY

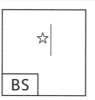 BS

 BR

HS	LY	BY	HR	LS
a	ⓑ	c	d	e

8.

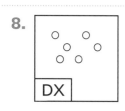 DX

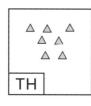 TH

 ZA

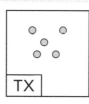 TX

 ZF

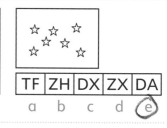

TF	ZH	DX	ZX	DA
a	b	c	d	ⓔ

9.

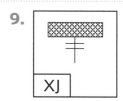 XJ

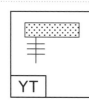 YT

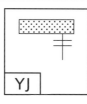 YJ

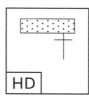 HD

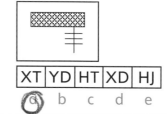

XT	YD	HT	XD	HJ
ⓐ	b	c	d	e

10.

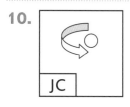 JC

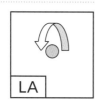 LA

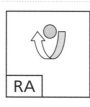 RA

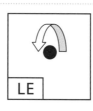 LE

LC	RE	JE	JA	RC
a	b	ⓒ	d	e

11.

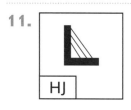 HJ

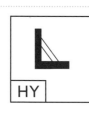 HY

 DY

 SP

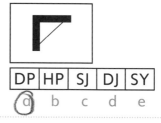

DP	HP	SJ	DJ	SY
ⓐ	b	c	d	e

12.

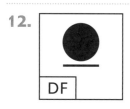 DF

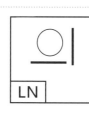 LN

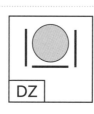 DZ

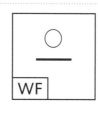 WF

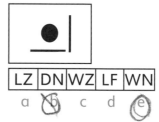

LZ	DN	WZ	LF	WN
a	b̶	c	d	ⓔ

End of test

Score:	Time taken:	Target met?

Which picture on the right best fits into the space in the grid? Circle the letter.

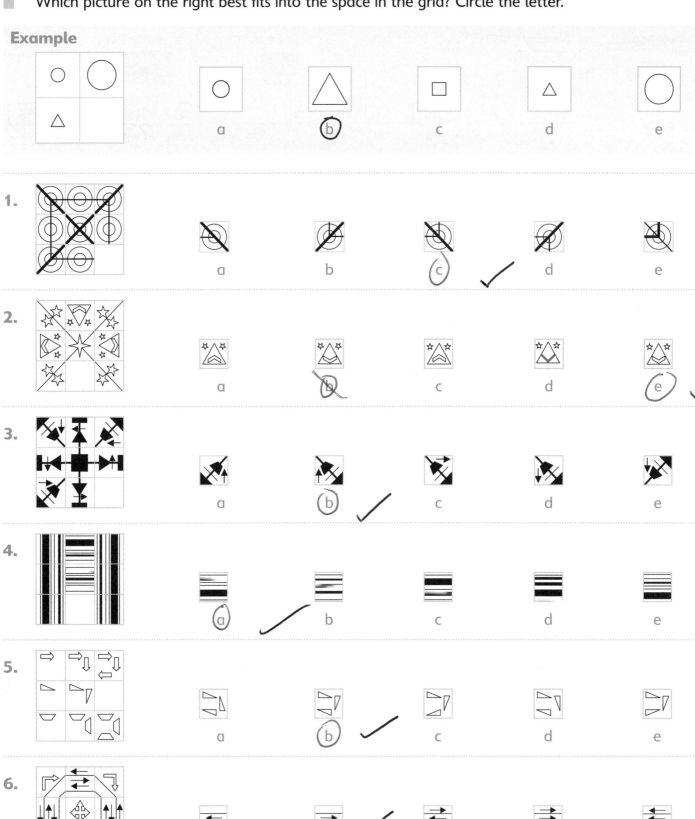

Example

a   b   c   d   e

1.   a   b   c   d   e

2.   a   b   c   d   e

3.   a   b   c   d   e

4.   a   b   c   d   e

5.   a   b   c   d   e

6.   a   b   c   d   e

Now go on to the next page ➡

Which cube can be made exactly from the net? Circle the letter.

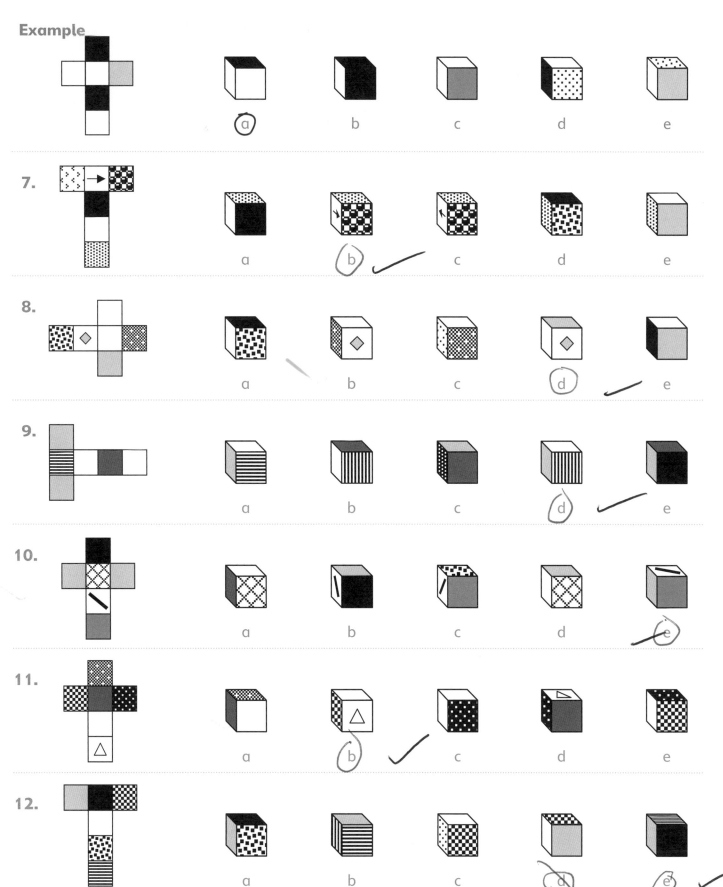

Example

7.

8.

9.

10.

11.

12.

End of test

| Score: | 12/12 | Time taken: | | Target met? | |

Non-verbal Reasoning Rapid Tests 4

23

Which picture on the right is a reflection of the picture on the left? Circle the letter.

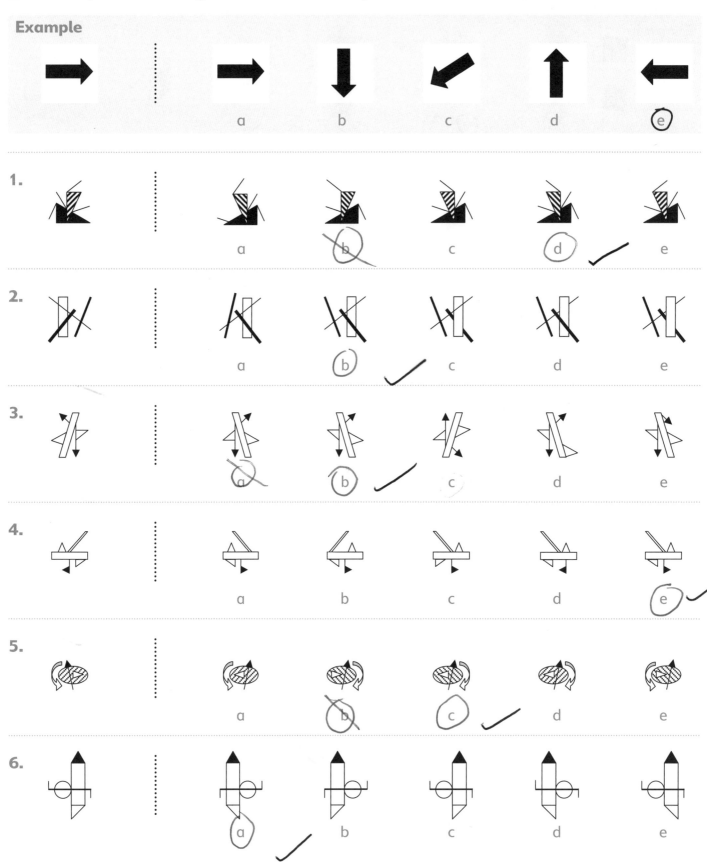

Now go on to the next page ➡

Which of the five pictures on the right goes with the third one to make a pair like the two on the left? Circle the letter.

Example

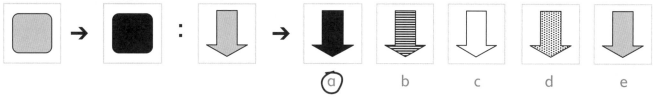

7.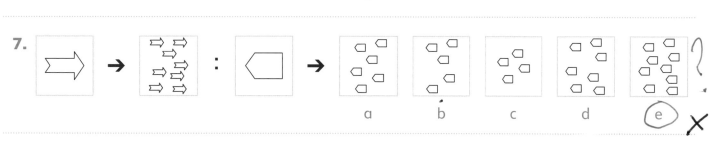

8.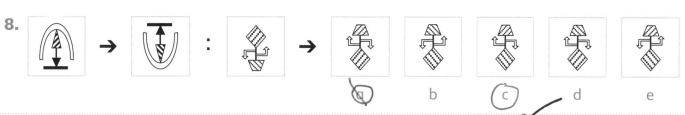

9.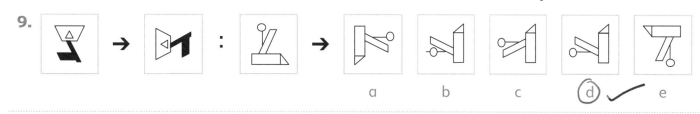

10.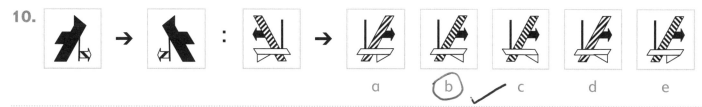

11.

12.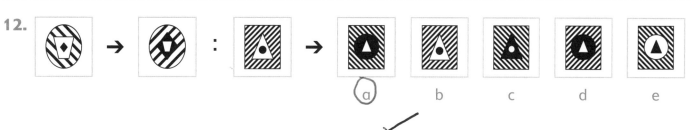

End of test

| Score: | \|\|/\|2 | Time taken: | | Target met? | |

Non-verbal Reasoning Rapid Tests 4

Target time: **7 minutes**

What is the code of the final picture? Circle the letter.

Example

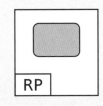 RP

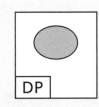 DP

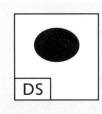 DS

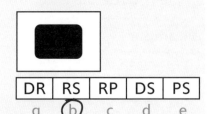

DR	RS	RP	DS	PS
a	ⓑ	c	d	e

1.

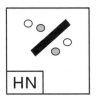 HN

 UD

 SD

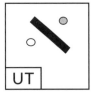 UT

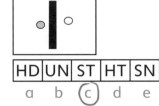

HD	UN	ST	HT	SN
a	b	©c	d	e

2.

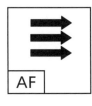 AF

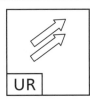 UR

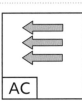 AC

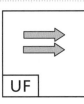 UF

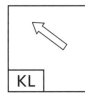 KL

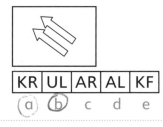

KR	UL	AR	AL	KF
ⓐ	ⓑ	c	d	e

3.

 RP

 BM

 ZS

 BP

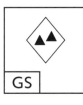 GS

GM	RS	BS	ZM	RP
a	b	c	ⓓ	e

4.

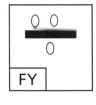 FY

 PC

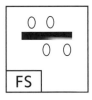 FS

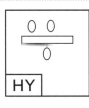 HY

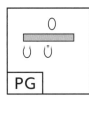 PG

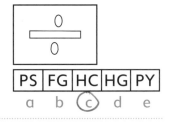

PS	FG	HC	HG	PY
a	b	©c	d	e

5.

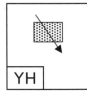 YH

 PL

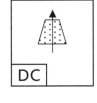 DC

 SX

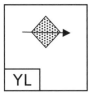 YL

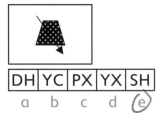

DH	YC	PX	YX	SH
a	b	c	d	ⓔ

6.

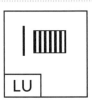 LU

 GH

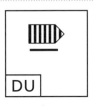 DU

 GA

 WK

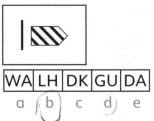

WA	LH	DK	GU	DA
a	ⓑ	c	d	e

Now go on to the next page ➡

Which picture on the right belongs to the group on the left? Circle the letter.

Example

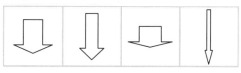

a   b   ⓒ   d   e

7.

a   b   c   d   e

8.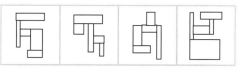

a   b   c   d   e

9.

a   ⓑ   c   d   e

10.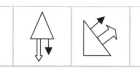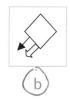

a   ⓑ   c   d   e

11.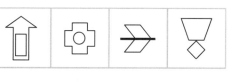

a   b   ⓒ   d   ⓔ

12.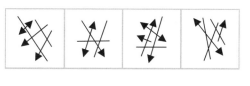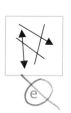

ⓐ   b   c   d   ⓔ

End of test

Score:		Time taken:		Target met?	

Target time: **7 minutes**

Which picture is the odd one out? Circle the letter.

Example

a   b   c   d   e

1.

a   b   c   d   e

2.

a   b   c   d   e

3.

a   b   c   d   e

4.

a   b   c   d   e

5.

a   b   c   d   e

6.

a   b   c   d   e

Now go on to the next page ➡

Which picture on the right goes in the empty space? Circle the letter.

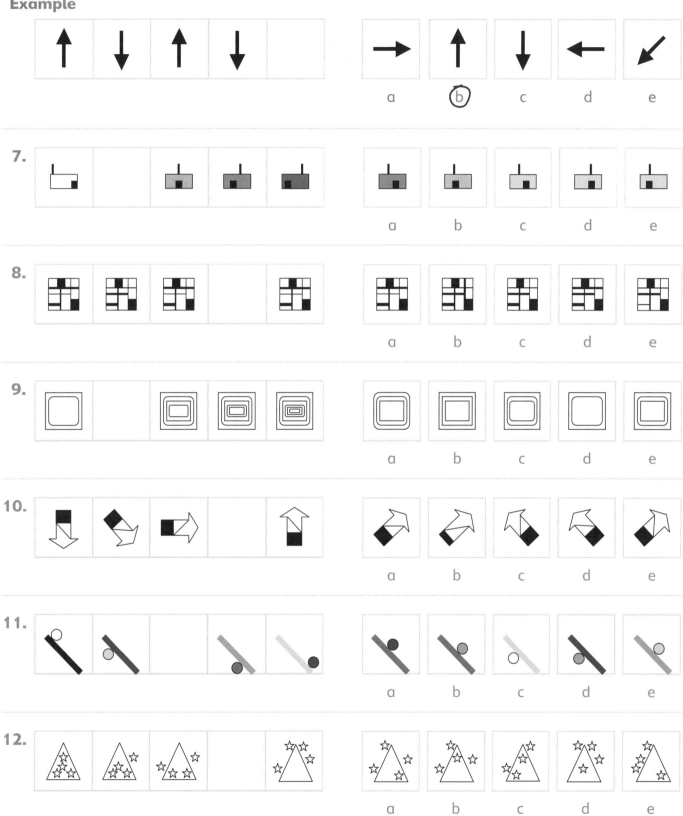

Target time: **7 minutes**

 In which picture on the right is the picture on the left hidden? Circle the letter.

Example

	a	b	c	d	e

1.

a   b   c   d   e

2.

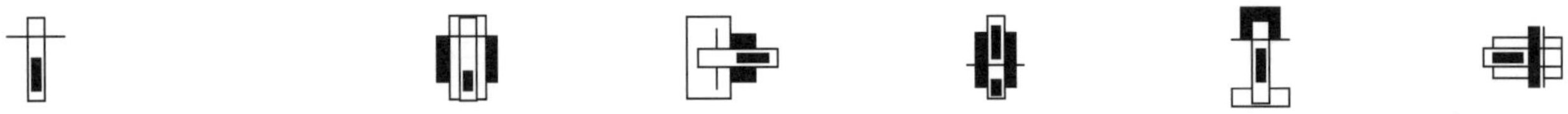

a   b   c   d   e

3.

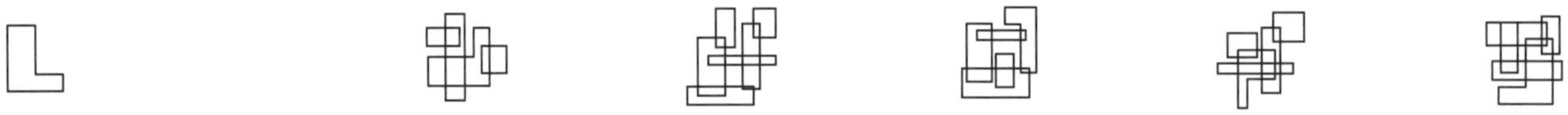

a   b   c   d   e

4.

a   b   c   d   e

5.

a   b   c   d   e

6.

a   b   c   d   e

Now go on to the next page ➡

Schofield & Sims

Which picture on the right best fits into the space in the grid? Circle the letter.

Example

  a ⓑ c d e

7.  a b c d e

8. 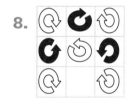 a b c d e

9. 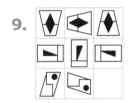 a b c d e

10.  a b c d e

11. 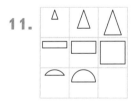 a b c d e

12. 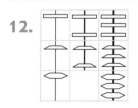 a b c d e

End of test

Score:		Time taken:		Target met?	

Target time: **7 minutes**

Which net can be made exactly from the cube? Circle the letter.

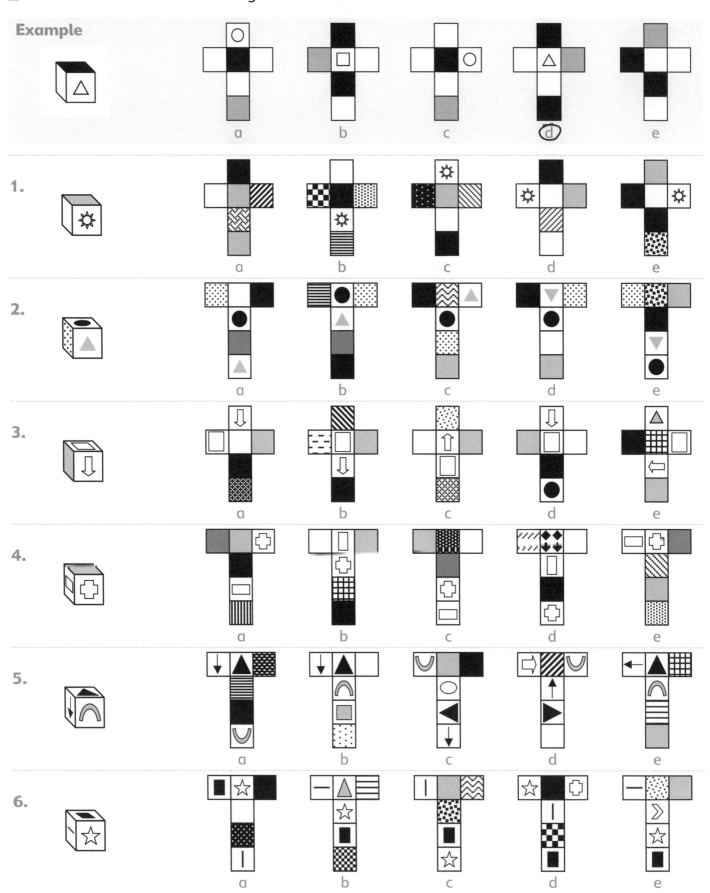

Example

a   b   c   d   e

1.

a   b   c   d   e

2.

a   b   c   d   e

3.

a   b   c   d   e

4.

a   b   c   d   e

5.

a   b   c   d   e

6.

a   b   c   d   e

Now go on to the next page ➡

Which picture on the right can be made by combining the first two shapes? Circle the letter.

Example

 =

a   b   ⓒ   d   e

7. 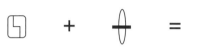 =

a   b   c   d   e

8.   =

a   b   c   d   e

9. =

a   b   c   d   e

10. =

a   b   c   d   e

11. =

a   b   c   d   e

12. =

a   b   c   d   e

End of test

Score:		Time taken:		Target met?	

Target time: **7 minutes**

Which picture on the right goes in the empty space? Circle the letter.

Example

 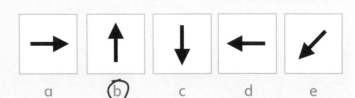

1.

 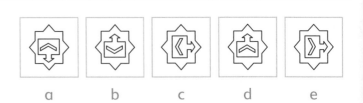

2.

 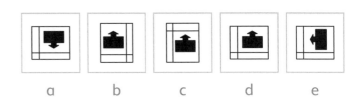

3.

 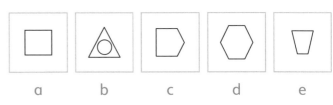

4.

 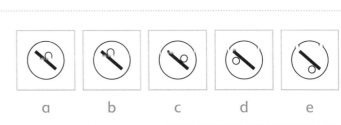

5.

 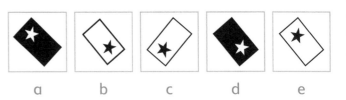

6.

 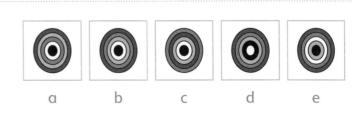

Now go on to the next page ➡

Schofield & Sims

Which picture on the right is a reflection of the picture on the left? Circle the letter.

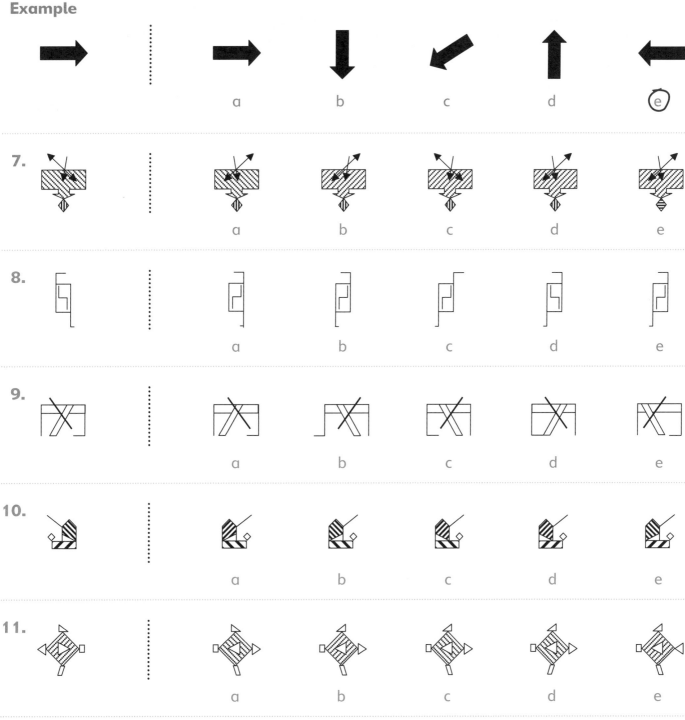

Example

a   b   c   d   (e)

7.

a   b   c   d   e

8.

a   b   c   d   e

9.

a   b   c   d   e

10.

a   b   c   d   e

11.

a   b   c   d   e

12.

a   b   c   d   e

End of test

Score:		Time taken:		Target met?	

What is the code of the final picture? Circle the letter.

Example

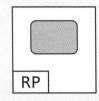 RP

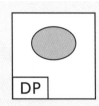 DP

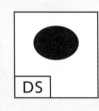 DS

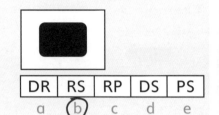

DR	RS	RP	DS	PS
a	b	c	d	e

1.

 BZ

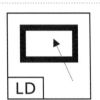 LD

 SC

 BF

 HD

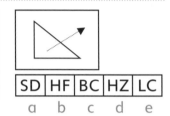

SD	HF	BC	HZ	LC
a	b	c	d	e

2.

 PE

 AW

 NE

 PH

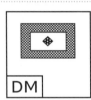 DM

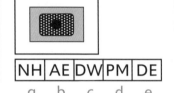

NH	AE	DW	PM	DE
a	b	c	d	e

3.

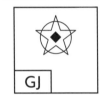 GJ

 WC

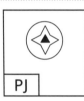 PJ

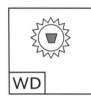 WD

 PH

PC	GC	WH	PD	GD
a	b	c	d	e

4.

 FP

 RD

 AH

 FN

 MP

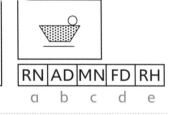

RN	AD	MN	FD	RH
a	b	c	d	e

5.

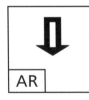 AR

 YD

 PV

 AV

 QD

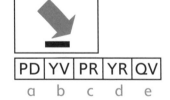

PD	YV	PR	YR	QV
a	b	c	d	e

6.

 WY

 TU

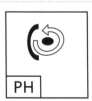 PH

 TS

 ZY

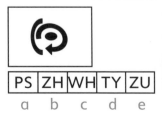

PS	ZH	WH	TY	ZU
a	b	c	d	e

Now go on to the next page ➡

Schofield & Si...

Which picture on the right best fits into the space in the grid? Circle the letter.

Example

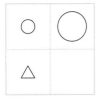   a   b   c   d   e

7. 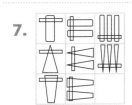   a   b   c   d   e

8. 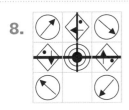   a   b   c   d   e

9. 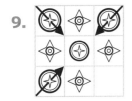   a   b   c   d   e

10. 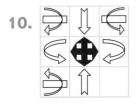   a   b   c   d   e

11. 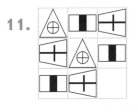   a   b   c   d   e

12. 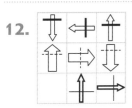   a   b   c   d   e

End of test

Score:		Time taken:		Target met?	

Which picture on the right belongs to the group on the left? Circle the letter.

Example

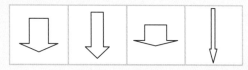

a   b   ⓒ   d   e

1.

a   b   c   d   e

2.

a   b   c   d   e

3.

a   b   c   d   e

4.

  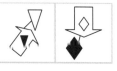

a   b   c   d   e

5.

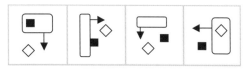

a   b   c   d   e

6.

a   b   c   d   e

Now go on to the next page ➡

Which of the five pictures on the right goes with the third one to make a pair like the two on the left? Circle the letter.

Example

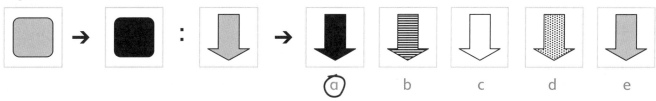

7.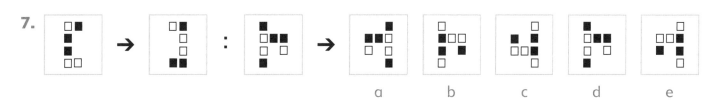

8.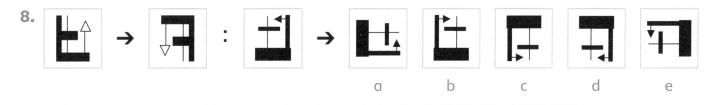

9.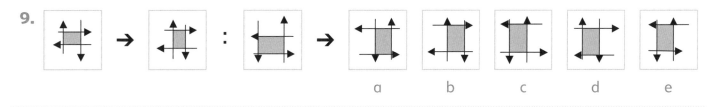

10.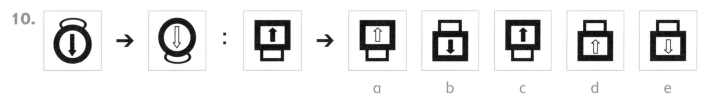

11.

12.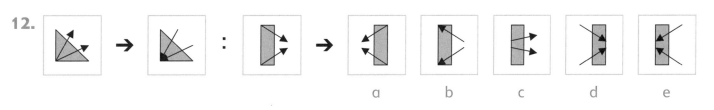

End of test

| **Score:** | | **Time taken:** | | **Target met?** | |

Progress chart

Write the score (out of 12) for each test in the box provided on the right of the graph.
Then colour in the row next to the box to represent this score.

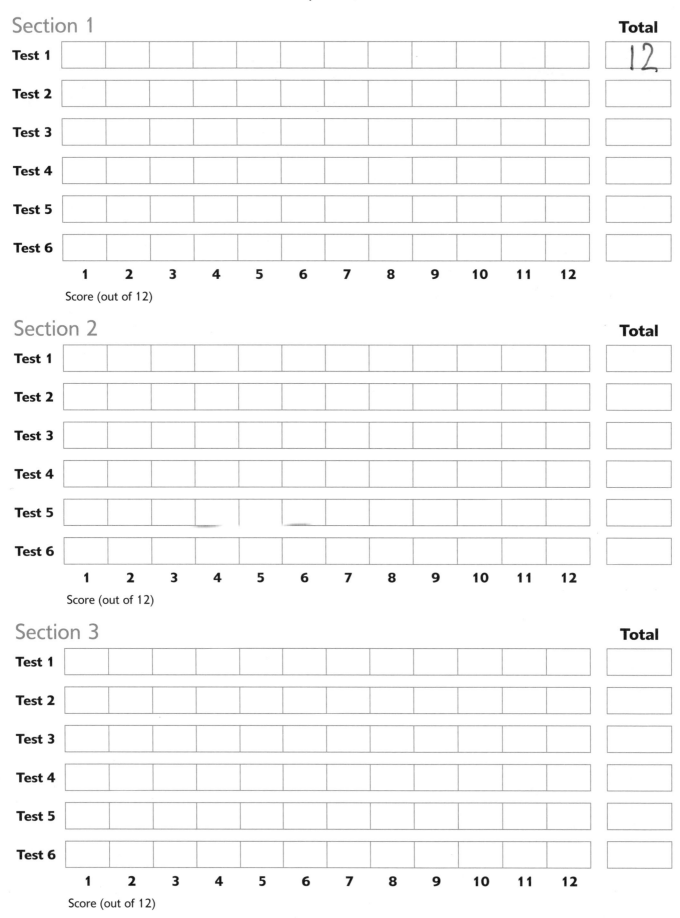

Section 1

												Total
Test 1												12
Test 2												
Test 3												
Test 4												
Test 5												
Test 6												

1   2   3   4   5   6   7   8   9   10   11   12
Score (out of 12)

Section 2

												Total
Test 1												
Test 2												
Test 3												
Test 4												
Test 5												
Test 6												

1   2   3   4   5   6   7   8   9   10   11   12
Score (out of 12)

Section 3

												Total
Test 1												
Test 2												
Test 3												
Test 4												
Test 5												
Test 6												

1   2   3   4   5   6   7   8   9   10   11   12
Score (out of 12)